At the

By Janice Behrens

ISBN: 978-1-338-88870-6

Editor: Liza Charlesworth
Art Director: Tannaz Fassihi; Designer: Tanya Chernyak
Photos ©: cover: Holly Kuchera/Shutterstock.com; 4: Cheryl Casey/Shutterstock.com.
All other photos © Getty Images.

1 2 3 4 5 6 7 8 9 10 68 31 30 29 28 27 26 25 24 23

Printed in Jiaxing, China. First printing, January 2023.

SCHOLASTIC INC.

Today is the day.
Let's go to the fair.
We can go on a ride there.
Wheeeeee!

Today is the day.
Let's go to the fair.
We can see a sheep there.
Baa!

Today is the day.
Let's go to the fair.
We can eat corn there.
Yum!

Today is the day.
Let's go to the fair.
We can drive a car there.
Vroom!

Today is the day.
Let's go to the fair.
We can play a game there.
Bop!

Today is the day.
Let's go to the fair.
We can jump up and down there.
Boing!

Tonight is the night.
Let's go to the fair.
We can see fireworks there.
Boom! Boom! Wow!